EDITH NEWLIN CHASE   YOLAINE LEFEBVRE

Secret Dawn

Scholastic Canada Ltd.

Scholastic Canada Ltd.
123 Newkirk Road, Richmond Hill, Ontario, Canada L4C 3G5

Scholastic Inc.
555 Broadway, New York, NY 10012, USA

Scholastic Australia Pty Limited
PO Box 579, Gosford, NSW 2250, Australia

Scholastic New Zealand Limited
Private Bag 94407, Greenmount, Auckland, New Zealand

Scholastic Ltd.
Villiers House, Clarendon Avenue, Leamington Spa, Warwickshire CV32 5PR, UK

The illustrations for this book were painted in watercolours.
The artist drops her colours on soaking wet paper,
letting them flow and blend freely. This technique is called "wet on wet."
For reference, photographs were used,
including some of the author's daughter and home.

The book was designed in Quark XPress, with type set in 24-point Giovanni Book.

Canadian Cataloguing in Publication Data
Chase, Edith Newlin
Secret dawn
A poem.
ISBN 0-590-12403-4
1. Children's poetry, American. I. Lefebvre, Yolaine,
1950- . II. Title.
PZ8.3.C35Se 1998 j811.54 C97-931129-2

5 4 3 2 1   Printed and bound in Canada   8 9 / 9
by DW Friesen

When the first thin light comes creeping
    Up the early edge of day,
And the household still is sleeping,
    Then I dress and slip away
To the place that I am keeping
    For my secret hideaway.

Stealing toward the giant billow
    Of a tree across the lawn,
Like a leafy mammoth pillow
    In the dim delight of dawn,
Up I climb into my willow
    While the night is hardly gone.

Up in the willow is wispy and whispery,
    Silent and silvery, misty with mystery!

Nobody else in the world is awake!
    Nobody knows how the little leaves quake.
Nobody knows that the willow is mine.
    Nobody knows of my shadowy shrine.
Nobody knows of the place where I hide
    My mystery box with treasure inside.
Nobody knows of my notebook thin
    Nor the stub of a pencil for writing in
The secret thoughts and the secret rhymes
    That I think to myself and write sometimes.

Nobody knows of my favourite tree
    Where we are alone — my secret and me!

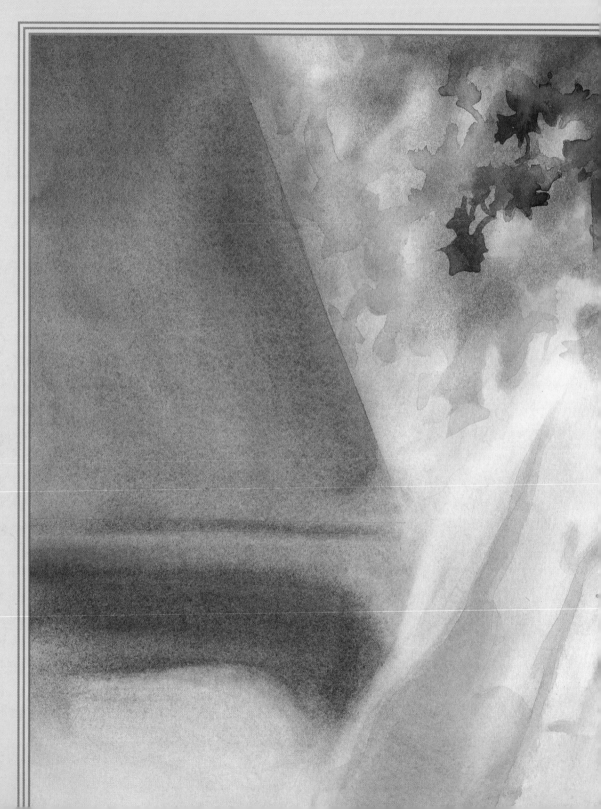

$\mathcal{W}$hen the first thin light comes creeping

up the early edge of day,

and the household still is sleeping,

then I dress and slip away

to the place that I am keeping

for my secret hideaway.

Stealing toward the giant billow

of a tree across the lawn,

like a leafy mammoth pillow

in the dim delight of dawn,

up I climb into my willow

while the night is hardly gone.

Up in the willow is wispy and whispery,

silent and silvery, misty with mystery!

Nobody else in the world is awake!

Nobody knows how the little leaves quake.

Nobody knows that the willow is mine.

Nobody knows of my shadowy shrine.

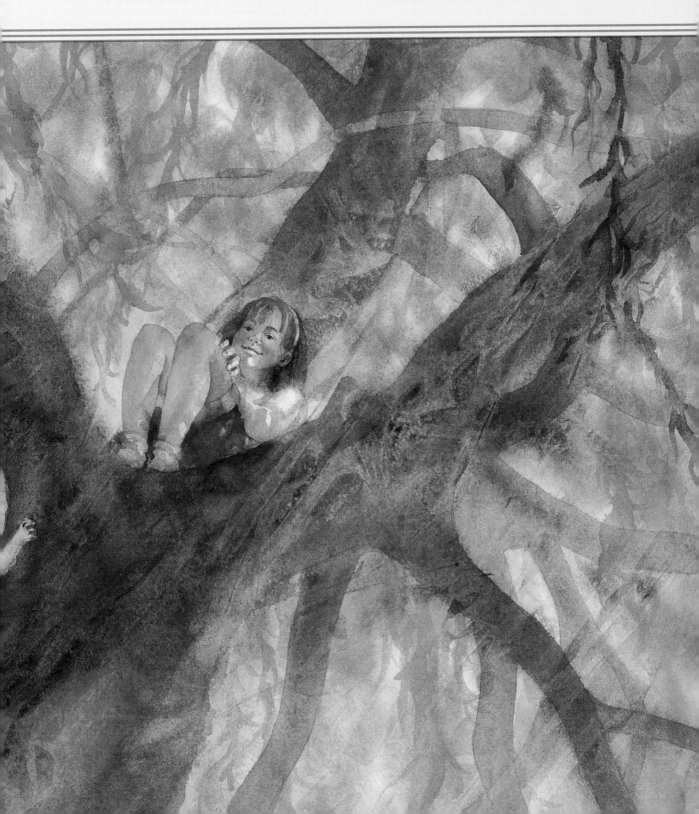

Nobody knows of the place where I hide

my mystery box with treasure inside.

Nobody knows of my notebook thin

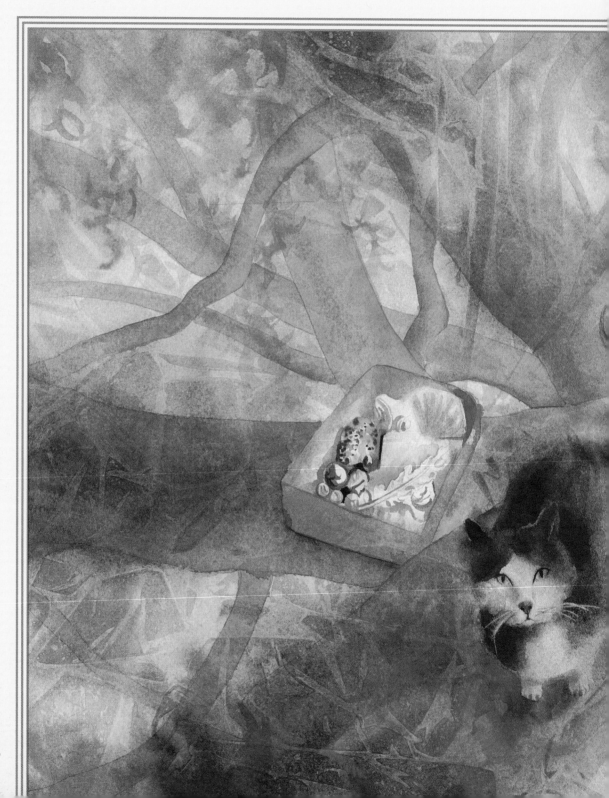

nor the stub of a pencil for writing in

the secret thoughts and the secret rhymes

that I think to myself and write sometimes.

Nobody knows of my favourite tree

where we are alone —

my secret and me!